# Initial
# DRUMS

GW00568142

TRINITY
COLLEGE LONDON

# THE EXAM
# AT A GLANCE

For your Rock & Pop exam you will need to perform a set of **three songs** and one of the **Session skills** assessments, either **Playback** or **Improvising**. You can choose the order in which you play your set-list.

## Song 1

Choose a song from this book

**OR** from www.trinityrock.com

## Song 2

Choose a different song from this book

**OR** from www.trinityrock.com

**OR** perform a song you have chosen yourself: this could be your own cover version or a song you have written. It should be at the same level as the songs in this book. See the website for detailed requirements.

## Song 3: Technical focus

Choose one of the Technical focus songs from this book, which cover three specific technical elements.

## Session skills

Choose either **Playback** or **Improvising**.

When you are preparing for your exam please check on **www.trinityrock.com** for the most up-to-date information and requirements as these can change from time to time.

# CONTENTS

Each song has two backing tracks: the first includes a click track to play along with, the second omits the click track.

Trinity College London's Rock & Pop syllabus and supporting publications have been devised and produced in association with Faber Music and Peters Edition London.

Trinity College London
89 Albert Embankment
London SE1 7TP UK
T + 44 (0)20 7820 6100
F + 44 (0)20 7820 6161
E music@trinitycollege.co.uk
www.trinitycollege.co.uk

Registered in the UK. Company no. 02683033
Charity no. 1014792
Patron HRH The Duke of Kent KG

Copyright © 2012 Trinity College London
Second impression, March 2013

Cover and book design by Chloë Alexander
Brand development by Andy Ashburner @ Caffeinehit (www.caffeinehit.com)
Photographs courtesy of Rex Features Limited.
Printed in England by Caligraving Ltd

Audio produced, mixed and mastered by Tom Fleming
Drums arranged by George Double
Backing tracks arranged by Tom Fleming

**Musicians**
Vocals: Bo Walton, Brendan Reilly & Alison Symons
Keyboards: Oliver Weeks
Guitar: Tom Fleming
Bass: Ben Hillyard
Drums: George Double
Studio Engineer: Joel Davies www.thelimehouse.com

ISBN: 978-0-85736-245-2

4/7/15

BAND OPTION

# SONGS BLACK BETTY

**Lead Belly**
New Words and New Music Arrangement by Huddie Ledbetter

♩ = 88 **Blues rock** *2 bars count-in*

**Chorus**
*vocal cue*
"Woah Black Betty..."

**Intro**

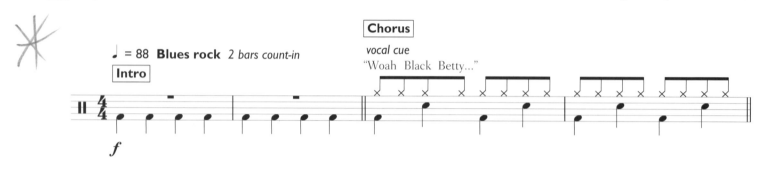

**Verse 1**

*vocal cue*
5 "She's from Birmingham..."

**Chorus**
*vocal cue*
"Woah Black Betty..."

8

**Verse 2**

*vocal cue*
11 "Looky here Black Betty..."

**Chorus**
*vocal cue*
"Woah Black Betty..."

R L R L R

15

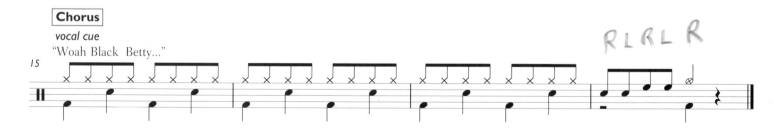

23/9/15

# SONGS BOULEVARD OF BROKEN DREAMS

**Green Day**

Words and Music by Billie Joe Armstrong, Frank E. Wright III and Michael Pritchard

♩ = 84 **Solid** *2 bars count-in*

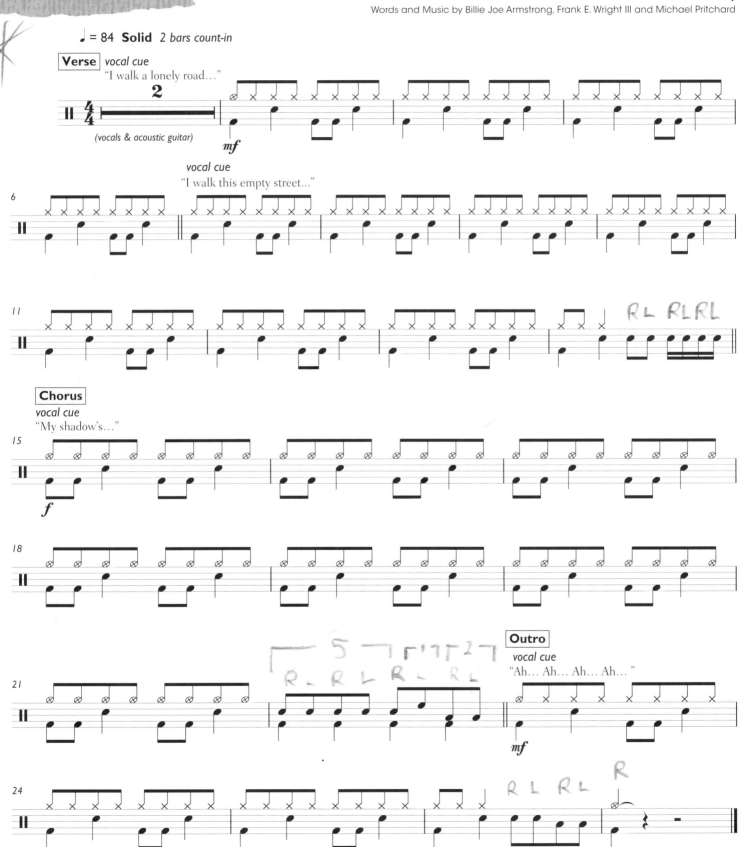

# SONGS I AM THE MUSIC MAN

demo backing
8 with click
9 without click

**Black Lace**
Trad.

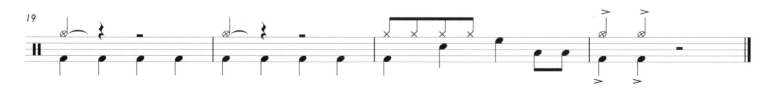

# SONGS AND THE CRADLE WILL ROCK

**Van Halen**

Words and Music by Edward Van Halen, Alex Van Halen, Michael Anthony and David Lee Roth

♩ = 108 **Classic Rock**   *2 bars count-in*

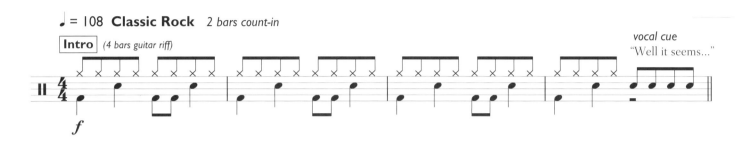

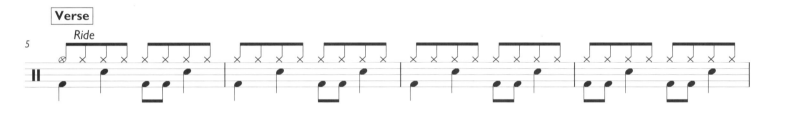

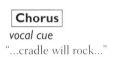

# DAYS

In your exam, you will be assessed on the following elements:

## 1 Cross-sticks

The opening groove (a section with the same repeated rhythm) in bars 2–10 of this arrangement uses a cross-stick (sometimes known as a rim-tap or rim-knock) in the right hand on beats 2 and 4. The stick can either be turned round or as normal. Make sure that this is well-controlled. Check that:

- there is a gap between the nearside rim and the end of the stick which is nearest the body
- this part of the stick remains in contact with the drum head throughout the stroke.

## 2 Ride cymbal

The chorus uses the ride cymbal. Make sure that you strike it really cleanly – and not too heavily – so that it vibrates well, making a full, resonant sound.

## 3 Fills

Stay very steady on the fills (short decorative passages that fill gaps between repeated patterns) – take care not to rush.

Play right in the centre of the toms for a full sound.

On the final fill, make the *crescendo* very gradual, so that every note is louder than the last one. That way it will sound really effective.

# TECHNICAL FOCUS SONGS

# DAYS

TRACK 13
demo

TRACK 14-15
backing
**14** with click
**15** without click

**Kirsty MacColl**
Words and Music by Ray Davies

# I'M GONNA BE (500 MILES)

In your exam, you will be assessed on the following technical elements:

## 1 Producing a good sound

This song has a strong backbeat (the backbeats are beats 2 and 4 of each bar). Concentrate on playing these well – you can really bring the song to life if you get the feel just right. Remember that the bass drum is also known as the 'kick' drum – give it a solid stroke! Experiment with how tightly together you are squeezing the hi-hat cymbals: try to find a really nice sound.

## 2 Playing a groove

During the chorus, the drums keep time by playing a simple groove (a groove is a section with the same repeated rhythm). Have fun with the splash of cymbal sound at the end of each bar but be careful not to overdo it – it should not sound too distracting!

## 3 Co-ordinating the bass and snare drums

Verse 2 is a march-like section in which the player can decide on the sticking. But, however you choose to play it, make sure that the bass drum and snare drum fit neatly together as written (you should hear one combined sound rather than two).

If one hand is louder than the other, the music will not flow smoothly so listen very carefully and watch that your stroke heights are consistently matched.

demo backing
**17** with click
**18** without click

# I'M GONNA BE (500 MILES)

**The Proclaimers**
Words and Music by Charles Reid and Craig Reid

# BLACK BETTY

**Lead Belly**

'Black Betty' is an African-American worksong (an early type of black American music sung rhythmically while doing manual labour). Nobody really knows who Black Betty was, but many believe that the name was slang for a prison bullwhip or a bottle of whisky.

'Black Betty' is normally credited to Lead Belly, although he was not the first to record it. Born Huddie Ledbetter, Lead Belly was a wandering musician who spent more than one spell in prison, including a long stretch for murder. His talent as a folk-blues singer and 12-string guitarist was recognised by the folk-music researcher and collector John Lomax, who later secured his release from prison (although he was soon back inside for assault). Lead Belly's songs have been recorded by Pete Seeger, Lonnie Donegan, The Fall and Nick Cave. The most famous recording of 'Black Betty' was by Ram Jam – it was their only hit.

---

**PERFORMANCE HINTS & TIPS**

'Black Betty' opens with a straight ♩ pattern on the bass drum. Make sure you keep a steady beat. After the short intro, 'Black Betty' uses two different patterns:

- The first pattern (in the chorus) is a straight ♪ groove:

Rather than play all the hi-hat notes exactly evenly, you could make the rhythm flow musically by emphasising the main beats a little.

- In the second pattern (in the verses) the hi-hat plays an off-beat ♪ pattern, which gives a double-time feel.

Make sure that the off-beat ♫ are even and definite. Practise dividing the beat exactly in half and keep your off-beats flowing precisely. Remember that they are much more likely to drag than rush.

"Oh *she* make me *sing*"

# BOULEVARD OF BROKEN DREAMS

**Green Day**

Green Day is a three-piece Californian pop punk band – Billie Joe Armstrong (vocals and guitar), Mike Dirnt (bass and backing vocals) and Tre Cool (drums). They came from the underground Californian punk scene but have gone on to enjoy mainstream success with catchy pop-rock songs.

'Boulevard of Broken Dreams' is from the 2004 concept album *American Idiot*, which tells the story of a character named Jesus of Suburbia.

The straight ♪ pattern in the chorus of 'Boulevard of Broken Dreams' has one hand playing the crash cymbal. Aim for a consistent sound, with the hand coming fully off the cymbal between strokes.

In bars 14 and 22 there are some fills (short decorative passages that fill gaps between repeated patterns). These should be played as alternate single strokes: e.g. RIGHT LEFT RIGHT LEFT, etc. Try to match the height of your strokes in both hands – make sure that your weaker hand is rising as high as your stronger one – so that the single strokes are equally balanced.

*'I walk a lonely road'*

# I AM THE MUSIC MAN

**Black Lace**

The origins of 'I Am The Music Man' are uncertain. It is usually sung as an action song where the singers act out playing the different instruments and sometimes imitate the sound of the instruments as well. In 1990 it was recorded by the British pop group Black Lace.

The drums play a straight $\frac{4}{4}$ beat for most of the song. Make sure that you keep the rhythm steady.

In bars 9 and 21 there are some fills (short decorative passages that fill gaps between repeated patterns). When you break from your repeated pattern to move around the drums, be extra careful not to speed up. Sometimes having to change co-ordination can distract from the pulse of the music.

Watch out for the repeat signs.

'I can *play* yes I *can* play'

# AND THE CRADLE WILL ROCK

**Van Halen**

Van Halen was a Californian band formed by brothers Eddie Van Halen (guitar and keyboards) and Alex Van Halen (drums). Their father was a musician and they both had classical training. Van Halen was one of the most successful heavy metal bands, renowned for loud distorted guitars, powerful bass riffs and flamboyant singing.

'And The Cradle Will Rock' is from the 1980 album *Women and Children First*, where Van Halen first experimented with synthesisers. It was the first song they released that featured the keyboard playing of Eddie Van Halen, who was already famous for his virtuosic guitar playing.

**PERFORMANCE · HINTS & TIPS ·**

Make sure that you keep in time with the guitar riff in the intro.

For most of the song, 'And The Cradle Will Rock' uses a straight ♪ pattern on the hi-hat or ride cymbal, together with the bass and snare drum pattern: ♩ ♩ ♫ ♩

'And The Cradle Will Rock' features drum fills (short decorative passages that fill gaps between repeated patterns). There are ♪ fills:
- on the snare at bars 4, 12 and 16
- around the drums at bar 20.

These should be played as single strokes (RIGHT LEFT RIGHT LEFT, etc.). Try to match the height of your strokes in both hands – make sure that your weaker hand is rising as high as your stronger one – so that the single strokes are equally balanced.

*'Well* they say *it's* kinda *frightnin'*

# ABOUT THE SONGS

# DAYS

**Kirsty MacColl**

Kirsty MacColl, daughter of the folk singer Ewan MacColl, enjoyed success both as an accomplished songwriter and as a vocalist. She had several pop hits during the 1980s and 1990s and also sang on recordings by other bands including the Smiths and the Pogues. Her life and career was cut short by a tragic accident when she was hit by a speedboat.

'Days' was originally a hit for the Kinks in 1969: it was written by their singer Ray Davies. Kirsty MacColl's recording – on her album *Kite* – made the song a hit again, 20 years after it was written.

'Days' is marked 'Not heavy'. Play with the tip (not the side) of your stick on the hi-hat so that you get a clean, light sound.

Remember that the repeated hi-hat ♪♪♪♪ should not sound mechanical – emphasise the stronger beats a little to make it sound more musical.

'I won't *forget* a single *day believe* me'

# I'M GONNA BE (500 MILES)

**The Proclaimers**

'I'm Gonna Be (500 Miles)' was written and performed by the Scottish duo The Proclaimers – identical twins Craig and Charlie Reid. It is from *Sunshine on Leith* (1988) – an album of catchy post-punk songs about love, life and politics in Scotland.

The song did not enjoy success until it was used in the 1993 film *Benny & Joon*, when it became a worldwide hit. Since then, it has been used in advertisements, films, and on television worldwide. It is very popular in Scotland where it is played at major sporting events every time the national team scores.

'I'm Gonna Be (500 Miles)' has two dynamic markings – these tell you how loudly or softly to play. Look out for these markings:

- ***mf*** *(mezzo forte* = moderately loudly)
- ***f*** *(forte* = loudly).

Verse 1 has drum beats on the first two beats of the bar and rests on the third and fourth beats. Be careful not to rush the rests.

'I'm *gonna* be the one who goes along with *you*'

# SESSION SKILLS

# PLAYBACK

For your exam, you can choose either Playback or Improvising (see page 19).
If you choose Playback, you will be asked to play some music you have not seen
or heard before.

In the exam, you will be given the song chart and the examiner will play a recording
of the music. You will hear several two-bar phrases on the recording: you should play
each of them straight back in turn. There's a rhythm track going throughout, which
helps you keep in time. There should not be any gaps in the music.

In the exam you will have two chances to play with the recording:
*   First time – for practice
*   Second time – for assessment.

You should listen to the audio, copying what you hear; you can also read the music
from the song chart. Here are some practice song charts – which are also on the CD
in this book.

Don't forget that the Improvising test can include requirements which may not be
shown in these examples, including those from earlier grades. Check the parameters
at www.trinityrock.com to prepare everything which might come up in your exam.

## Practice playback 1

## Practice playback 2

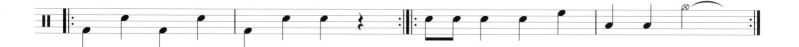

# IMPROVISING

For your exam, you can choose either Playback (see page 18), or Improvising. If you choose to improvise, you will be asked to improvise over a backing track that you haven't heard before in a specified style.

In the exam, you will be given a song chart and the examiner will play a recording of the backing track. The backing track consists of a passage of music played on a loop. You should improvise a drum beat over it.

In the exam you will have two chances to play with the recording:
- First time – for practice
- Second time – for assessment.

Here are some improvising charts for practice which are also on the CD in this book.

Don't forget that the Improvising test can include requirements which may not be shown in these examples, including those from earlier grades. Check the parameters at www.trinityrock.com to prepare everything which might come up in your exam.

## Practice improvisation 1

♩ = 102 **Rock**

| Em | Am | G | Em |

## Practice improvisation 2

♩ = 60 **Slow Pop**

| Am | Em | D | C |

# CHOOSING A SONG FOR YOUR EXAM

There are lots of options to help you choose your three songs for the exam.
For Songs 1 and 2, you can choose a song which is:

- from this book
- from www.trinityrock.com

Or for Song 2 you can choose a song which is:

- sheet music from a printed or online source.
- your own arrangement of a song or a song you have written yourself (see page 21).

You can play the song unaccompanied or with a backing track (minus the solo instrument). If you like, you can create a backing track yourself (or with friends), or you could add your own vocals – or both.

For Initial, the song should be between 30 seconds and two minutes long, and the level of difficulty should be similar to your other songs.
When choosing a song, think about:

- Does it work on my instrument?
- Are there any technical elements that are too difficult for me? (If so, perhaps save it for when you do the next grade.)
- Do I enjoy playing it?
- Does it work with my other songs to create a good set-list?

See www.trinityrock.com for information and advice on choosing your own song.

## SHEET MUSIC

You must always bring an original copy of the book or a download sheet with email certificate for each song you perform in the exam. If you choose to write your own song you must provide the examiner with a copy of the sheet music. Your music can be:

- a lead sheet with lyrics, chords and melody line
- a chord chart with lyrics
- a full score using conventional staff notation
- see page 21 for details on presenting a song you have written yourself.

The title of the song and your name should be on the sheet music.

# WRITING YOUR OWN SONG

You can play a song that you have written yourself for one of the choices in your exam. For Initial, your song should last between 30 seconds and two minutes, so it is likely to be quite straightforward. It is sometimes difficult to know where to begin, however. Here are some suggestions for starting points:

- **A melody**: many songs are made up around a 'hook' (a short catchy melodic idea, usually only a few notes long).
Try writing a couple of ideas for hooks here:

- **A chord sequence**: a short chord sequence can provide an entire verse or chorus. Write your ideas for a chord sequence here:

‖ | | | | | | | |

- **A rhythm**: a short repeated rhythm will often underpin an entire song.
Think of a couple of short rhythms you could use here:

## WRITING YOUR SONG DOWN

Rock and pop music is often written as a **lead sheet** with the lyrics (if there are any), chords and a melody line.

- As a drummer, you may want to write your part using **drum notation**, used for the songs in this book. There is a guide to this notation on page 24.

- You can, if you prefer, use a **graph** or **table** to represent your music, as long as it is clear to anyone else (including the examiner) how the song goes.

There are plenty of other ways of starting: perhaps with a riff or a lyric, for example.

You will also need to consider the **structure** of your song (verse and chorus, 12-bar blues, and so on), the **style** it is in (blues, hard rock, etc.), and what **instruments** it is for (e.g. voice/keyboards/drums . . .).

There are many choices to be made – which is why writing a song is such a rewarding thing to do.

# PLAYING IN A BAND

Playing in a band is exciting: it can be a lot of fun and, as with everything, the more you do it, the easier it gets. It is very different from playing on your own. Everyone contributes to the overall sound: the most important skill you need to develop is listening.

For a band to sound good, the players need to be 'together' – that mainly means keeping in time with each other, but also playing at the same volume, and with the same kind of feeling.

Your relationship with the other band members is also important. Talk with them about the music you play, the music you like, and what you'd like the band to achieve short-term and long-term.

Band rehearsals are important – you should not be late, tired or distracted by your mobile phone! Being positive makes a huge difference. Try to create a friendly atmosphere in rehearsals so that everybody feels comfortable trying out new things. Don't worry about making mistakes: that is what rehearsals are for.

'Black Betty' (page 4) and 'I Am The Music Man' (page 6) are arranged for band. You will find parts for vocals, keyboards, guitar and bass in the other Trinity Rock & Pop Initial books. Trinity offers exams for groups of musicians at various levels. The songs arranged for bands are ideal to include as part of a song-list for these exams. Have look at the website for more details.

## HINTS AND TIPS

- When you are starting out, it is easier if you have only one of each instrument, so that you can hear clearly what everybody is playing.

- Record your practice sessions and listen back for sections that worked well and bits that had problems.

- Meet up regularly to socialise before and after rehearsals to help keep in touch with each other.

# PLAYING WITH BACKING TRACKS

The CD contains demos and backing tracks of all the songs in the book. The additional songs at www.trinityrock.com also come with demos and backing tracks.

- In your exam, you should play with the backing track, or you can create your own (see below).
- The backing tracks start with a click track, which sets the tempo and helps you start accurately.
- Be careful to set the balance between the volume of the backing track and your instrument.
- Listen carefully to the backing track to ensure you are playing in time.

If you are creating your own backing track here are some further tips:
- Make sure the sound quality is of a good standard.
- Think carefully about the instruments/sounds you are putting on the backing track.
- Avoid copying what you are playing on the backing track – it should support not duplicate.
- Do you need to include a click track at the beginning?

## COPYRIGHT IN A SONG

If you are a singer or songwriter it is important to know about copyright. When someone writes a song or creates an arrangement they own the copyright (sometimes called 'the rights') to that version. The copyright means that other people cannot copy it, sell it, perform it in a concert, make it available online or record it without the owner's permission or the appropriate licence. When you write a song you automatically own the copyright to it, which means that other people cannot copy your work. But just as importantly, you cannot copy other people's work, or perform it in public without their permission or the appropriate licence.

**Points to remember**
- You can create a cover version of a song for an exam or other non-public performance.
- You cannot record your cover version and make your recording available to others (by copying it or uploading it to a website) without the appropriate licence.
- You own the copyright of your own original song, which means that no one is allowed to copy it.
- You cannot copy someone else's song without their permission or the appropriate licence.
- If you would like to use somebody else's words in your own song you must check if they are in copyright and, if so, we recommend you confirm with the author that they are happy for the words to be used as lyrics.
- Materials protected by copyright can normally be used as lyrics in our examinations as these are private performances under copyright law. The examiner may ask you the name of the original author in the exam.
- When you present your own song to the examiner make sure you include the title, the names of any writers and the source of your lyrics.

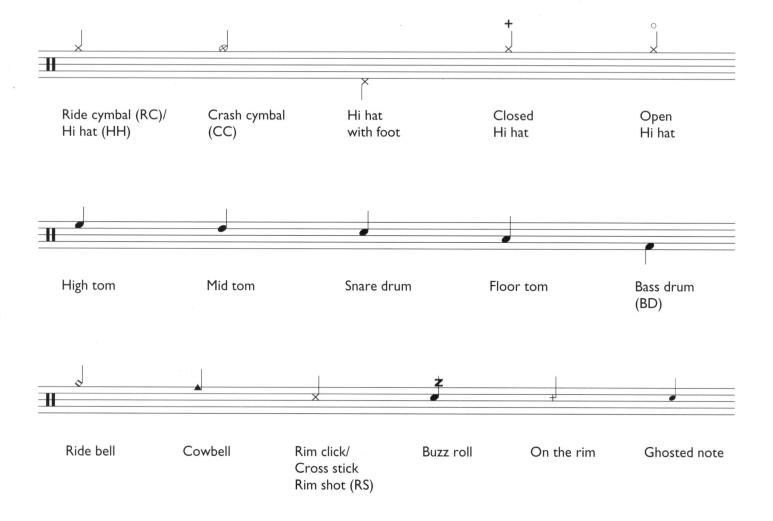

Ride cymbal (RC)/ Hi hat (HH)    Crash cymbal (CC)    Hi hat with foot    Closed Hi hat    Open Hi hat

High tom    Mid tom    Snare drum    Floor tom    Bass drum (BD)

Ride bell    Cowbell    Rim click/ Cross stick Rim shot (RS)    Buzz roll    On the rim    Ghosted note